Eat to the Beat

Columbus, OH

The McGraw·Hill Companies

SRAonline.com

 SRA

Printed in China.

Send all inquiries to:
SRA/McGraw-Hill
8787 Orion Place
Columbus, OH 43240-4027

ISBN: 0-07-605630-9

1 2 3 4 5 6 7 8 9 NOR 12 11 10 09 08 07 06

The *McGraw-Hill* Companies

Josh had been working on a plan from the first moment he saw the sign announcing his school's talent show. He had three weeks to decide what he would do for the show. He knew most of the students would sing, dance, act, and play the usual instruments—guitar, trumpet, violin, and so on. So Josh decided to choose a performance that was truly unique. At least fifty students would perform, he guessed. He could easily blend into the crowd and make little or no impression if he was not careful.

The first thing Josh considered was a stand-up routine. He would write his own material instead of repeating the jokes of famous comics. However, after a day of writing unfunny jokes, he discarded that idea. He thought getting his pet, Sam, to do tricks might be fun. Unfortunately, Sam was a hamster that could not be trained. Josh ran through a number of ideas—magic act, mime, plate spinning—but each came with a hurdle that was too high. He was putting another bad idea to rest when Ms. Abdel, his music teacher, stopped at his table in the library after school.

"That's a nice rumba beat you have there, Josh," she said.

He looked at her blankly.

"Your pencil—you're tapping out a rumba. It's a style of music for a Cuban dance."

"Really?" replied Josh. "I didn't know I was doing that. I'm trying to think of something to do for the talent show, but I'm running out of ideas."

"Why not play your guitar? You're quite good."

"Thank you, Ms. Abdel, but I want to do something no one else is going to try. It's difficult to be remembered when you are one of eight guitarists."

"I see your point."

Ms. Abdel lingered at Josh's desk for a few moments. Then she spoke again.

"Maybe your pencil can help with your project." Josh hoped she would explain her remark, and she quickly did. "Almost anything can be used to create music. You can scratch or bang on all sorts of things to create rhythm. And to create melody, you can use a variety of objects, making sure each one emits a unique note. Why don't you try something similar to your pencil tapping, but on a larger scale, for the talent show?"

Josh thought it was an intriguing idea. He asked Ms. Abdel if she had any suggestions.

"Well," she began, "wet glasses have been used to create music. If you slide a finger around the rims, they give off pleasant tones. Thinner glasses work best, and different shapes and sizes will create different notes.

"Even the same glass can produce different notes. It depends on how much water is in each glass. Benjamin Franklin actually invented an instrument called the glass harmonica that used this idea."

"If I can find a design online, maybe I can build one," Josh thought aloud.

Ms. Abdel chuckled. "Probably not—it was a pretty complicated contraption. You could use other, simpler things. For instance, people in jug bands blow across the tops of jugs to keep the beat. Blow across the top of an empty bottle; you'll get an idea of the sound. Jug bands also use washboards for percussion.

"Once I even saw a woman play a large saw like it was a string instrument. She held the saw against one leg. Then she dragged a bow across the edge of the blade. The thin sheet of metal vibrated. It created an eerie effect. I remember the sound sending shivers down my spine.

"Classical composers sometimes use peculiar instruments. The most famous composer to do this is probably Tchaikovsky. One section of his *1812 Overture* is often performed with cannon blasts. The modern composer John Cage wrote one piece that's four minutes and thirty-three seconds of a pianist sitting at a piano and not playing. Instead of listening to the music, you listen to the noises you usually disregard."

"So what should I try?" Josh asked.

"I don't want to influence your choice too much," Ms. Abdel explained. "I think you need to listen to the sounds around you. When you hear the right one, you'll find a way to use it."

That evening Josh and his parents went out for dinner. Through the entire meal Josh barely spoke a word. He was enthralled by the various sounds he might have simply ignored in the past. Chairs squeaked, and glasses clinked. A blender's muffled whirring came from the kitchen. A cart of dirty dishes clattered by between the tables. The steady noise of the conversations in the room grew louder, then quieter, then louder once again.

Josh thought he was actually starting to hear a rhythm within the random sounds. Then a dish's breaking in the kitchen snapped him back into the moment. He knew what he would do for the show.

The next day he asked
a few friends to help him.
They spent the following two
weeks practicing every day
after school. When the night
of the talent show arrived,
they felt confident that their
performance would be perfect.

Josh and his friends were
scheduled to perform last.
Just as Josh had predicted,
most of the students acted,
sang, danced, or played an
instrument. Some of them were
very good. None were unique
by Josh's standards. Luke
Smythe did a comedy routine
with his twin sister Lynn that
received big laughs. Josh was
glad he hadn't chosen to do his
tired jokes.

Josh and his friends made some last minute adjustments to their routine backstage. They felt confident they were ready. When the next-to-last performer was finished, Josh and his friends moved their set into place.

The audience watched as the curtain rose and exposed a restaurant scene assembled onstage. Josh stood holding a jug of water in front of a table lined with glasses. Four of his friends sat at tables. Two other friends stood nearby dressed as waiters. Microphones were hanging in the air and lying on the floor.

Josh's friend Julio slid his chair back from the table and made it squeak across the floor. A moment later he slid it forward again. He repeated this action over and over. Soon the girl sitting with him stirred her glass with a spoon. It made a high-pitched clinking sound that worked rhythmically with Julio's squeaking chair.

The waiter standing at the other table began scribbling on a pad of paper. A microphone hanging directly above him amplified the pencil's scratching sound. Then Josh began filling glasses with water. The liquidly soft sound contrasted nicely with the clinking, squeaking, and scratching created by his friends.

The rhythm became more and more complex as each new sound was added. Finally everyone onstage was contributing to the mix. After they had been playing for a few minutes, Josh's friend Steve came onstage. He carried a large stack of pots and pans that looked freshly washed. When he reached center stage, Steve pretended to trip. He sent the cookware flying, and pots and pans littered the area. The racket of crashing metal filled the theater and drowned out the other sounds. When the pots and pans came to a rest, the audience realized the performance had stopped.

The silence seemed eerie. Then the applause began. Josh and his friends exchanged triumphant looks and proudly took their bows.

At the award ceremony, they did not win first prize. That went to Juan Aldo for playing a beautiful song on his cello. However, Josh and his friends won a ribbon for "Most Imaginative Performance," which suited Josh just fine.

As he drove home with his parents, he was thinking ahead to next year's show. He liked the sound of the applause the piece had received. Maybe there was some way he could use applause to score the action in a new piece. He and his friends had a year to think about it.

Vocabulary

contraption (page 8) *n.* A device; a gadget.

eerie (page 8) *adj.* Scary; creepy.

classical (page 9) *adj.* Music or art created in the late eighteenth and early nineteenth centuries.

peculiar (page 9) *adj.* Strange; different; weird.

influence (page 9) *v.* To inspire; to give someone a reason for doing something.

enthralled (page 10) *adj.* Charmed; fascinated.

expose (page 12) *v.* To show to someone.

Comprehension Questions

1. From which point of view is this story told? How has the author made the point of view clear?

2. When did you monitor and adjust your reading speed? Why did you find it necessary to do so?